Conten

G000293662

Counting in 3s

Read the numbers on the banners.

Write in the missing numbers.

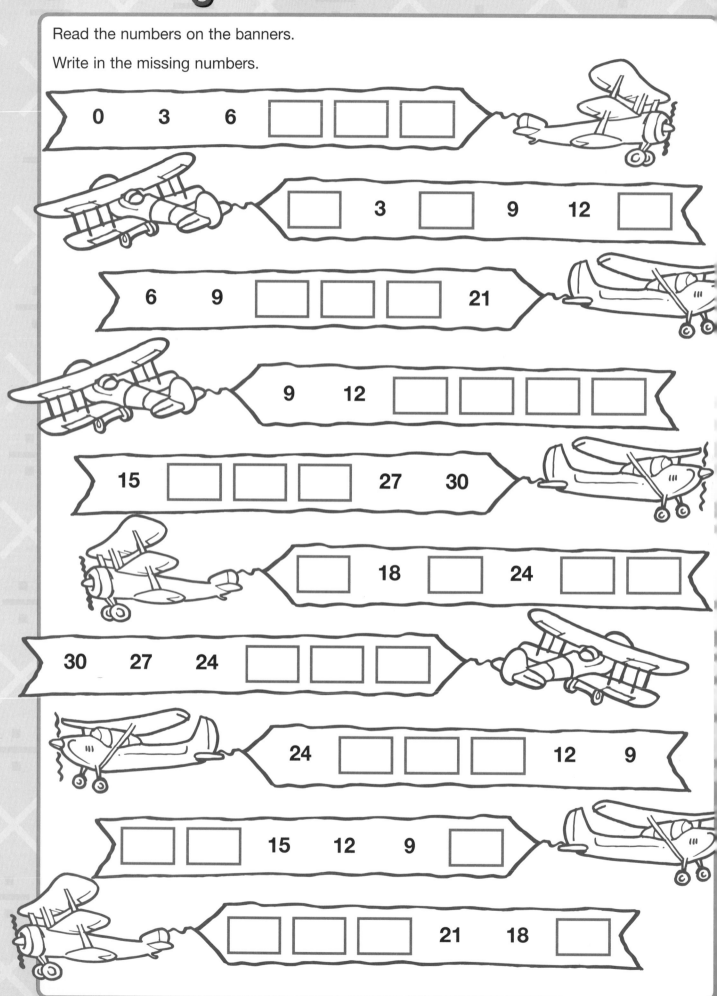

0   3   6   [ ] [ ] [ ]

[ ]   3   [ ]   9   12   [ ]

6   9   [ ] [ ] [ ]   21

9   12   [ ] [ ] [ ] [ ]

15   [ ] [ ] [ ]   27   30

[ ]   18   [ ]   24   [ ] [ ]

30   27   24   [ ] [ ] [ ]

24   [ ] [ ] [ ]   12   9

[ ] [ ]   15   12   9   [ ]

[ ] [ ] [ ]   21   18   [ ]

Schofield & Sims Times Tables Practice Book 2

Building the ×3 table

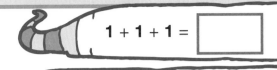

1 + 1 + 1 = ☐   **1** times **3** is ☐

2 + 2 + 2 = ☐   **2** times **3** is ☐

3 + 3 + 3 = ☐   **3** times **3** is ☐

4 + 4 + 4 = ☐   **4** times **3** is ☐

5 + 5 + 5 = ☐   **5** times **3** is ☐

6 + 6 + 6 = ☐   **6** times **3** is ☐

7 + 7 + 7 = ☐   **7** times **3** is ☐

8 + 8 + 8 = ☐   **8** times **3** is ☐

9 + 9 + 9 = ☐   **9** times **3** is ☐

10 + 10 + 10 = ☐   **10** times **3** is ☐

Write the answers to the ×3 table.

4 × 3 = ☐

1 × 3 = ☐

5 × 3 = ☐

8 × 3 = ☐

2 × 3 = ☐

9 × 3 = ☐

6 × 3 = ☐

3 × 3 = ☐

10 × 3 = ☐

7 × 3 = ☐

Multiplying by 3

Write the answers to these ×3 questions.

In

| 2 |
| 5 |
| 7 |
| 3 |
| 6 |
| 1 |
| 8 |
| 10 |
| 9 |
| 4 |

Out

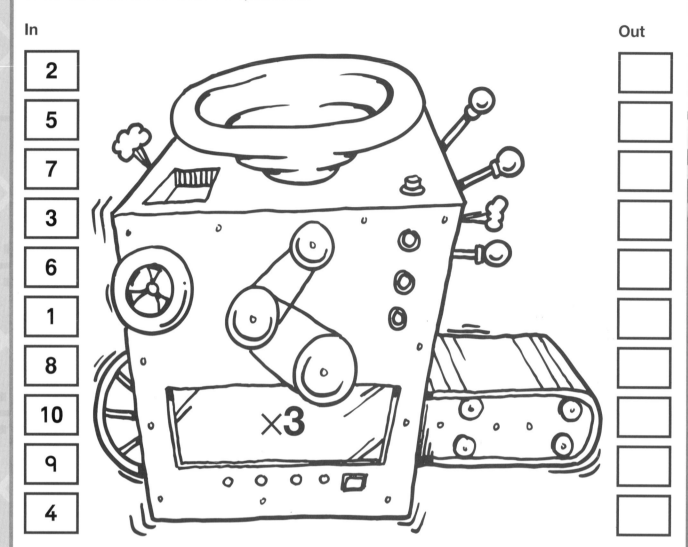

Write the ×3 table.

Write the table facts with odd answers in the Odd column.

Write the table facts with even answers in the Even column.

Remember:

Odd times odd gives odd answers.

Even times odd gives even answers.

Odd answer	Even answer

Dividing by 3

Use the pictures to help you.

Write the answers to these division questions.

3 cakes shared between 3 plates is ☐ each.

3 divided by 3 is ☐ .   3 ÷ 3 = ☐

6 cakes shared between 3 plates is ☐ each.

6 divided by 3 is ☐ .   6 ÷ 3 = ☐

9 cakes shared between 3 plates is ☐ each.

9 divided by 3 is ☐ .   9 ÷ 3 = ☐

12 cakes shared between 3 plates is ☐ each.

12 divided by 3 is ☐ .   12 ÷ 3 = ☐

15 cakes shared between 3 plates is ☐ each.

15 divided by 3 is ☐ .   15 ÷ 3 = ☐

18 cakes shared between 3 plates is ☐ each.

18 divided by 3 is ☐ .   18 ÷ 3 = ☐

21 cakes shared between 3 plates is ☐ each.

21 divided by 3 is ☐ .   21 ÷ 3 = ☐

24 cakes shared between 3 plates is ☐ each.

24 divided by 3 is ☐ .   24 ÷ 3 = ☐

27 cakes shared between 3 plates is ☐ each.

27 divided by 3 is ☐ .   27 ÷ 3 = ☐

30 cakes shared between 3 plates is ☐ each.

30 divided by 3 is ☐ .   30 ÷ 3 = ☐

Multiplying and dividing by 3

Draw a line to match the multiplication to its answer.

3×3 2×3 10×3 7×3

9×3 1×3

5×3 8×3 4×3 6×3

12   18   30   27

9   21   3

24   15

6

Write the answers to these division questions.

$6 \div 3 =$ ☐ $9 \div 3 =$ ☐ $30 \div 3 =$ ☐

$15 \div 3 =$ ☐ $12 \div 3 =$ ☐ $18 \div 3 =$ ☐

$21 \div 3 =$ ☐ $27 \div 3 =$ ☐ $24 \div 3 =$ ☐

$3 \div 3 =$ ☐

Schofield & Sims Times Tables Practice Book 2

Multiplying and dividing by 3

Read the question on the pirate.

Draw a line to the answer on the coin.

1

18

10×3

9×3

$3 \div 3$

9

3

$24 \div 3$

4

$15 \div 3$

30

$27 \div 3$

27

$30 \div 3$

$12 \div 3$

10

6

6×3

$18 \div 3$

9

5

1×3

8

4×3

3

8×3

7

2×3

5×3

6

$6 \div 3$

24

3×3

12

15

7×3

21

$21 \div 3$

$9 \div 3$

2

Multiplying and dividing by 2, 3, 5 and 10

Look at these function machines.

Write what is happening in the box.

The first one is done for you.

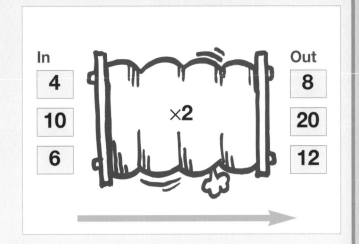

In		Out
4	×2	8
10		20
6		12

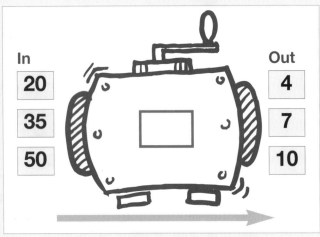

In		Out
20		4
35		7
50		10

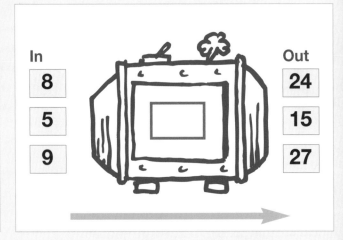

In		Out
8		24
5		15
9		27

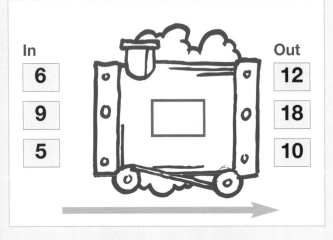

In		Out
6		12
9		18
5		10

In		Out
4		40
8		80
7		70

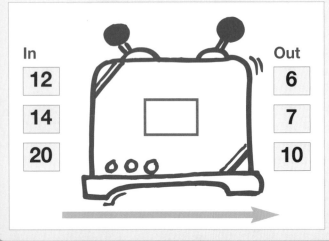

In		Out
12		6
14		7
20		10

In		Out
60		6
50		5
30		3

Schofield & Sims Times Tables Practice Book 2

Counting in 4s

Read the numbers.

Write in the missing numbers.

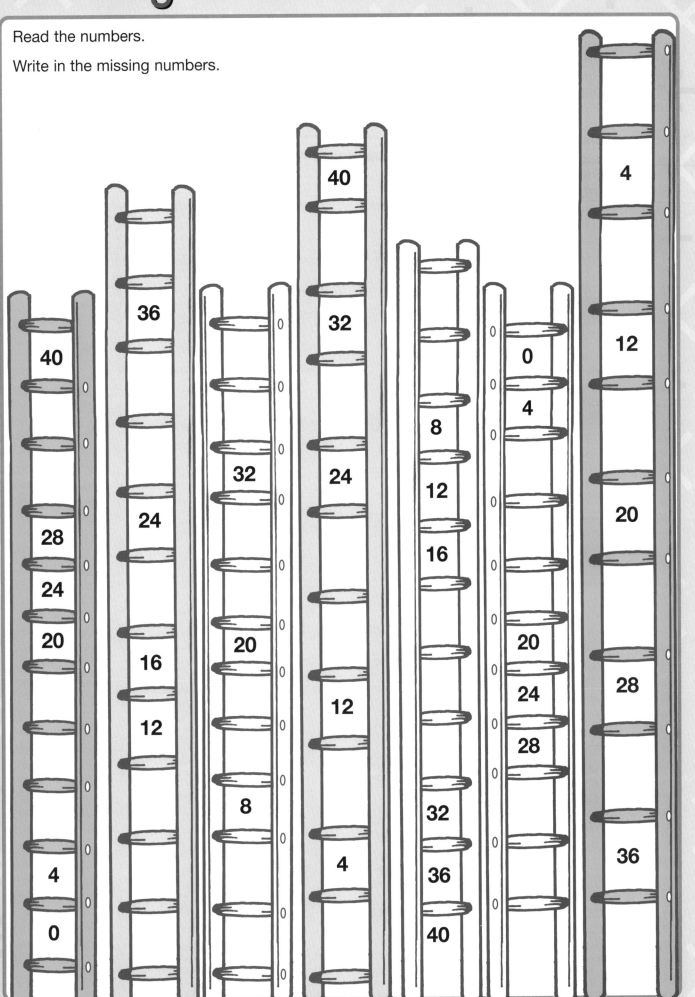

Building the x4 table

Write the answers in the boxes.

1 + 1 + 1 + 1 = ☐   1 times 4 is ☐

2 + 2 + 2 + 2 = ☐   2 times 4 is ☐

3 + 3 + 3 + 3 = ☐   3 times 4 is ☐

4 + 4 + 4 + 4 = ☐   4 times 4 is ☐

5 + 5 + 5 + 5 = ☐   5 times 4 is ☐

6 + 6 + 6 + 6 = ☐   6 times 4 is ☐

7 + 7 + 7 + 7 = ☐   7 times 4 is ☐

8 + 8 + 8 + 8 = ☐   8 times 4 is ☐

9 + 9 + 9 + 9 = ☐   9 times 4 is ☐

10 + 10 + 10 + 10 = ☐   10 times 4 is ☐

One way to learn your ×4 table is to double the ×2 table facts.

Complete this table.

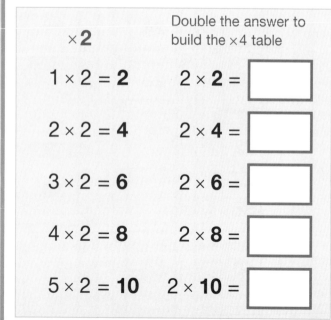

×2	Double the answer to build the ×4 table	×2	Double the answer to build the ×4 table
$1 \times 2 = 2$	$2 \times 2 =$ ☐	$6 \times 2 = 12$	$2 \times 12 =$ ☐
$2 \times 2 = 4$	$2 \times 4 =$ ☐	$7 \times 2 = 14$	$2 \times 14 =$ ☐
$3 \times 2 = 6$	$2 \times 6 =$ ☐	$8 \times 2 = 16$	$2 \times 16 =$ ☐
$4 \times 2 = 8$	$2 \times 8 =$ ☐	$9 \times 2 = 18$	$2 \times 18 =$ ☐
$5 \times 2 = 10$	$2 \times 10 =$ ☐	$10 \times 2 = 20$	$2 \times 20 =$ ☐

Multiplying by 4

Write the answers to these multiplications.

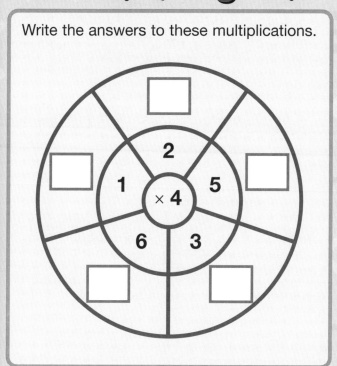

Write the answers to these multiplications.

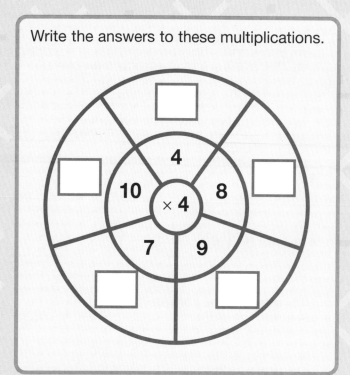

Here are some answers to the ×4 table.

Match each answer to its number sentence.

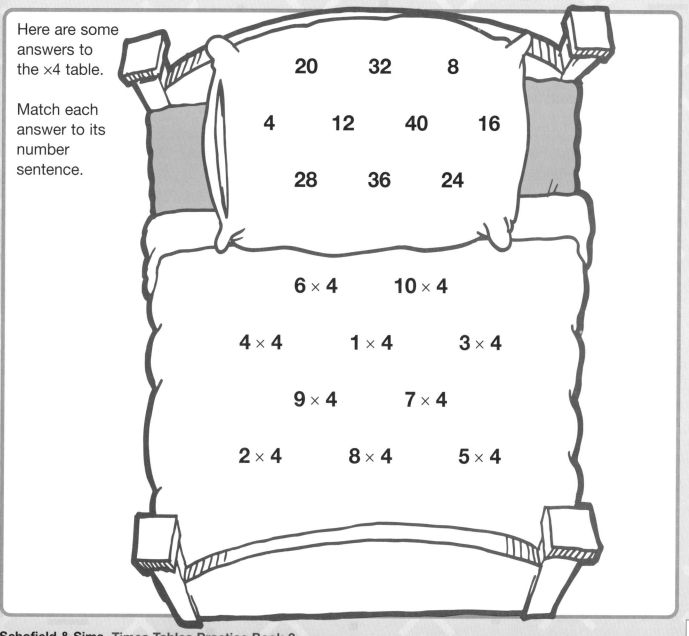

20	32	8
4	12	40	16
28	36	24

6 × 4   10 × 4

4 × 4   1 × 4   3 × 4

9 × 4   7 × 4

2 × 4   8 × 4   5 × 4

Dividing by 4

Use the pictures to help you.

Write the answers to these division questions.

4 beetles shared between 4 leaves is [ ] each.

4 divided by **4** is [ ] .   **4 ÷ 4 =** [ ]

8 beetles shared between 4 leaves is [ ] each.

8 divided by **4** is [ ] .   **8 ÷ 4 =** [ ]

12 beetles shared between 4 leaves is [ ] each.

12 divided by **4** is [ ] .   **12 ÷ 4 =** [ ]

16 beetles shared between 4 leaves is [ ] each.

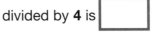 

16 divided by **4** is [ ] .   **16 ÷ 4 =** [ ]

20 beetles shared between 4 leaves is [ ] each.

20 divided by **4** is [ ] .   **20 ÷ 4 =** [ ]

24 beetles shared between 4 leaves is [ ] each.

24 divided by **4** is [ ] .   **24 ÷ 4 =** [ ]

28 beetles shared between 4 leaves is [ ] each.

28 divided by **4** is [ ] .   **28 ÷ 4 =** [ ]

32 beetles shared between 4 leaves is [ ] each.

32 divided by **4** is [ ] .   **32 ÷ 4 =** [ ]

36 beetles shared between 4 leaves is [ ] each.

  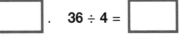

36 divided by **4** is [ ] .   **36 ÷ 4 =** [ ]

40 beetles shared between 4 leaves is [ ] each.

 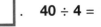

40 divided by **4** is [ ] .   **40 ÷ 4 =** [ ]

Multiplying and dividing by 4

Match the rocket to its star with a line.

Write the answers to these division questions.

1×4

5×4

28

4

2×4

7×4

32

20

4×4

8

24

9×4

8×4

6×4

40

16

3×4

12

36

10×4

$12 \div 4 =$

$4 \div 4 =$

$36 \div 4 =$

$28 \div 4 =$

$16 \div 4 =$

$20 \div 4 =$

$8 \div 4 =$

$24 \div 4 =$

$32 \div 4 =$

$40 \div 4 =$

Multiplying and dividing by 4

$6 \times 4 = \boxed{}$

$36 \div 4 = \boxed{}$ $1 \times 4 = \boxed{}$

$4 \div 4 = \boxed{}$ $9 \times 4 = \boxed{}$

$12 \div 4 = \boxed{}$ $20 \div 4 = \boxed{}$ $4 \times 4 = \boxed{}$

$8 \times 4 = \boxed{}$ $2 \times 4 = \boxed{}$

$28 \div 4 = \boxed{}$ $16 \div 4 = \boxed{}$ $8 \div 4 = \boxed{}$

$32 \div 4 = \boxed{}$ $24 \div 4 = \boxed{}$

$10 \times 4 = \boxed{}$ $3 \times 4 = \boxed{}$

$5 \times 4 = \boxed{}$ $40 \div 4 = \boxed{}$

$7 \times 4 = \boxed{}$

Write the answers to these word problems.

Morgan has **40p**. How many **4p** sweets can he buy?

$\boxed{}$

Chelsy wants **5** pencils. The pencils are **4p** each. How much will the pencils cost?

$\boxed{}$ p

There are **4** cakes on a plate. How many cakes are there on **6** plates?

$\boxed{}$

Karen wants to share **32** apples between **4** bowls. How many apples will there be in each bowl?

$\boxed{}$

Multiplying and dividing by 3 and 4

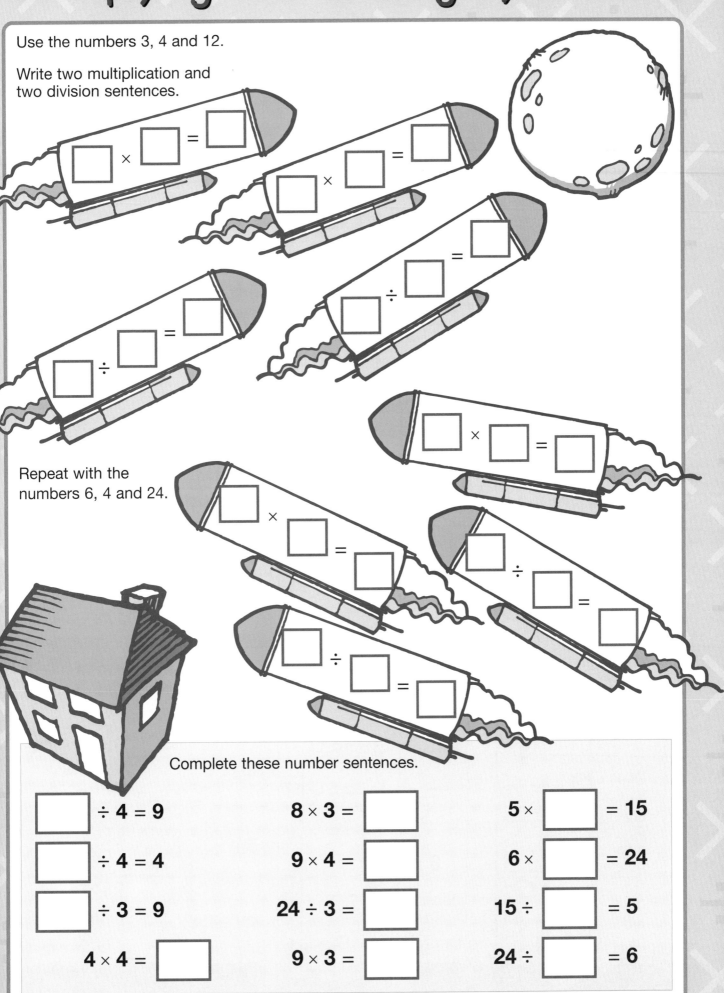

Use the numbers 3, 4 and 12.

Write two multiplication and two division sentences.

☐ × ☐ = ☐

☐ × ☐ = ☐

☐ ÷ ☐ = ☐

☐ ÷ ☐ = ☐

Repeat with the numbers 6, 4 and 24.

☐ × ☐ = ☐

☐ × ☐ = ☐

☐ ÷ ☐ = ☐

☐ ÷ ☐ = ☐

Complete these number sentences.

☐ ÷ 4 = 9   8 × 3 = ☐   5 × ☐ = 15

☐ ÷ 4 = 4   9 × 4 = ☐   6 × ☐ = 24

☐ ÷ 3 = 9   24 ÷ 3 = ☐   15 ÷ ☐ = 5

4 × 4 = ☐   9 × 3 = ☐   24 ÷ ☐ = 6

Counting in 6s

Read the numbers.

Write in the missing numbers.

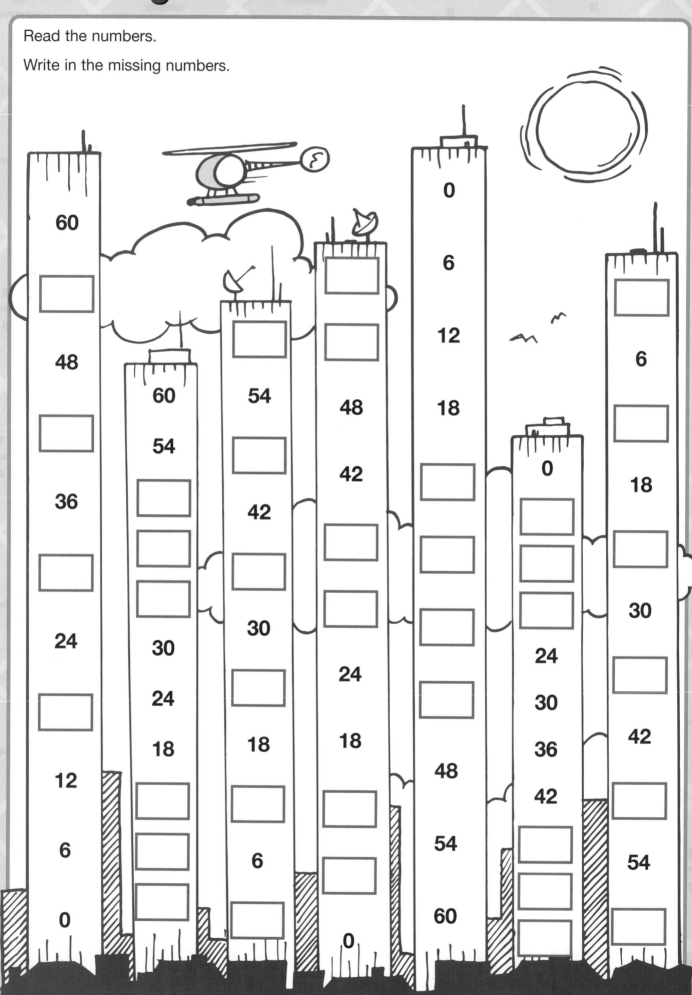

Building the x6 table

$1 + 1 + 1 + 1 + 1 + 1 =$ ☐   **1** times **6** is ☐

$2 + 2 + 2 + 2 + 2 + 2 =$ ☐   **2** times **6** is ☐

$3 + 3 + 3 + 3 + 3 + 3 =$ ☐   **3** times **6** is ☐

$4 + 4 + 4 + 4 + 4 + 4 =$ ☐   **4** times **6** is ☐

$5 + 5 + 5 + 5 + 5 + 5 =$ ☐   **5** times **6** is ☐

$6 + 6 + 6 + 6 + 6 + 6 =$ ☐   **6** times **6** is ☐

$7 + 7 + 7 + 7 + 7 + 7 =$ ☐   **7** times **6** is ☐

$8 + 8 + 8 + 8 + 8 + 8 =$ ☐   **8** times **6** is ☐

$9 + 9 + 9 + 9 + 9 + 9 =$ ☐   **9** times **6** is ☐

$10 + 10 + 10 + 10 + 10 + 10 =$ ☐   **10** times **6** is ☐

One way to learn your ×6 table is to double the ×3 table facts.

Complete this table.

×**3**	Double the answer to build the ×6 table	×**3**	Double the answer to build the ×6 table
$1 \times 3 = 3$	$2 \times 3 =$ ☐	$6 \times 3 = 18$	$2 \times 18 =$ ☐
$2 \times 3 = 6$	$2 \times 6 =$ ☐	$7 \times 3 = 21$	$2 \times 21 =$ ☐
$3 \times 3 = 9$	$2 \times 9 =$ ☐	$8 \times 3 = 24$	$2 \times 24 =$ ☐
$4 \times 3 = 12$	$2 \times 12 =$ ☐	$9 \times 3 = 27$	$2 \times 27 =$ ☐
$5 \times 3 = 15$	$2 \times 15 =$ ☐	$10 \times 3 = 30$	$2 \times 30 =$ ☐

Multiplying by 6

Write the answers to these multiplications.

In

| 8 |
| 4 |
| 5 |
| 1 |
| 6 |
| 7 |
| 3 |
| 10 |
| 9 |
| 2 |

Out

×6

Write the answers to these word problems.

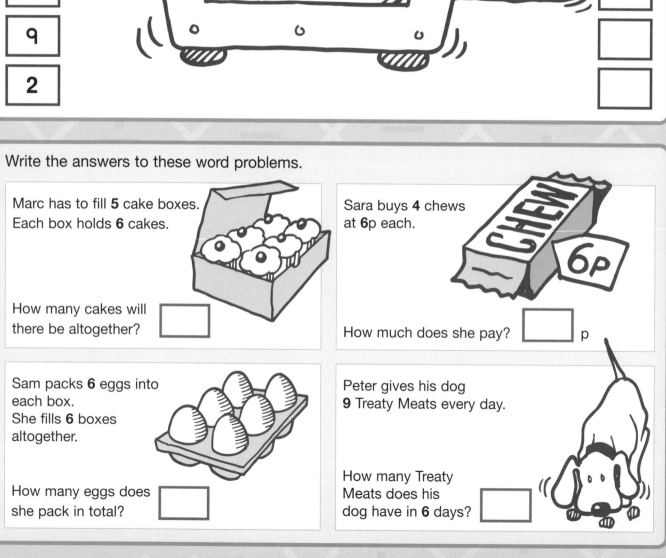

Marc has to fill **5** cake boxes.
Each box holds **6** cakes.

How many cakes will
there be altogether? ☐

Sara buys **4** chews
at **6**p each.

How much does she pay? ☐ p

Sam packs **6** eggs into
each box.
She fills **6** boxes
altogether.

How many eggs does
she pack in total? ☐

Peter gives his dog
9 Treaty Meats every day.

How many Treaty
Meats does his
dog have in **6** days? ☐

Schofield & Sims Times Tables Practice Book 2

Dividing by 6

Use what you know about multiplying by 6 to help you to answer these.

For example, if you know that 2 × 6 = 12 you can work out that 12 ÷ 6 = 2.

6 cakes shared between 6 plates is ☐ each.

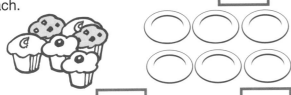

6 divided by **6** is ☐ .   **6 ÷ 6 =** ☐

12 cakes shared between 6 plates is ☐ each.

12 divided by **6** is ☐ .   **12 ÷ 6 =** ☐

18 cakes shared between 6 plates is ☐ each.

18 divided by **6** is ☐ .   **18 ÷ 6 =** ☐

24 cakes shared between 6 plates is ☐ each.

24 divided by **6** is ☐ .   **24 ÷ 6 =** ☐

30 cakes shared between 6 plates is ☐ each.

30 divided by **6** is ☐ .   **30 ÷ 6 =** ☐

36 cakes shared between 6 plates is ☐ each.

36 divided by **6** is ☐ .   **36 ÷ 6 =** ☐

42 cakes shared between 6 plates is ☐ each.

42 divided by **6** is ☐ .   **42 ÷ 6 =** ☐

48 cakes shared between 6 plates is ☐ each.

48 divided by **6** is ☐ .   **48 ÷ 6 =** ☐

54 cakes shared between 6 plates is ☐ each.

54 divided by **6** is ☐ .   **54 ÷ 6 =** ☐

60 cakes shared between 6 plates is ☐ each.

60 divided by **6** is ☐ .   **60 ÷ 6 =** ☐

Multiplying and dividing by 6

Write the answers.

$5 \times 6 =$

$2 \times 6 =$

$3 \times 6 =$

$6 \times 6 =$

$7 \times 6 =$

$8 \times 6 =$

$9 \times 6 =$

$4 \times 6 =$

$1 \times 6 =$

$10 \times 6 =$

There are **30** children in the class.
Their teacher wants to put them in groups of **6**.

How many groups will there be?

6 children sit at each lunch table. There are 6 tables.

How many children have lunch?

Each child has **8** coloured pencils. **6** children put their coloured pencils into one box.

How many coloured pencils are there?

There are **54** grapes to be shared between **6** children.

How many grapes does each child have?

Schofield & Sims Times Tables Practice Book 2

Multiplying and dividing by 6

Join the question to its answer.

18

3

$6 \div 6$

1×6

$48 \div 6$

6

$42 \div 6$

1

3×6

9

54

8

8×6

9×6

24

$30 \div 6$

7

$18 \div 6$

$12 \div 6$

$60 \div 6$

2

48

36

5

$54 \div 6$

4×6

6

30

6×6

18

$24 \div 6$

$36 \div 6$

7×6

10

12

60

4

5×6

3×6

10×6

42

2×6

Multiplying and dividing by 3, 4 and 6

Choose from these numbers.

Write 3 different multiplication sentences.

Write 3 different division sentences.

3   4   6   8   24

☐ × ☐ = ☐

☐ × ☐ = ☐

☐ × ☐ = ☐

☐ ÷ ☐ = ☐

☐ ÷ ☐ = ☐

☐ ÷ ☐ = ☐

Complete these number sentences. See how quickly you can do them.

$7 \times 3 =$ ☐ $4 \times 4 =$ ☐ $60 \div 6 =$ ☐

$7 \times 4 =$ ☐ $7 \times 6 =$ ☐ $18 \div 3 =$ ☐

$7 \times 6 =$ ☐ $15 \div 3 =$ ☐ $2 \times 4 =$ ☐

$36 \div 4 =$ ☐ $20 \div 4 =$ ☐ $9 \times 6 =$ ☐

$27 \div 3 =$ ☐ $36 \div 6 =$ ☐ $30 \div 3 =$ ☐

$54 \div 6 =$ ☐ $4 \times 3 =$ ☐ $40 \div 4 =$ ☐

$9 \times 3 =$ ☐ $28 \div 4 =$ ☐

Write how many minutes you took to complete these. ☐

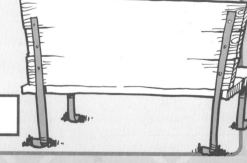

Schofield & Sims Times Tables Practice Book 2

Counting in 7s

Read the numbers.

Write in the missing numbers.

| 0 | 7 | 14 | | | |

| | | | 21 | 28 | 35 |

| | | | 35 | 42 | 49 |

| 14 | 21 | 28 | | | | 56 | 63 |

| | 28 | 35 | | | | | 70 |

| | | | 21 | 28 | | 42 | 49 | | | 70 |

| 70 | 63 | 56 | | | |

| | | 35 | 28 | 21 | 14 | 7 | 0 |

| 56 | 49 | 42 | | | | | |

| 70 | | | | | 35 | 28 | 21 | | | |

Building the ×7 table

Write the answers in the boxes.

1 + 1 + 1 + 1 + 1 + 1 + 1 =	☐	1 times 7 is ☐
2 + 2 + 2 + 2 + 2 + 2 + 2 =	☐	2 times 7 is ☐
3 + 3 + 3 + 3 + 3 + 3 + 3 =	☐	3 times 7 is ☐
4 + 4 + 4 + 4 + 4 + 4 + 4 =	☐	4 times 7 is ☐
5 + 5 + 5 + 5 + 5 + 5 + 5 =	☐	5 times 7 is ☐
6 + 6 + 6 + 6 + 6 + 6 + 6 =	☐	6 times 7 is ☐
7 + 7 + 7 + 7 + 7 + 7 + 7 =	☐	7 times 7 is ☐
8 + 8 + 8 + 8 + 8 + 8 + 8 =	☐	8 times 7 is ☐
9 + 9 + 9 + 9 + 9 + 9 + 9 =	☐	9 times 7 is ☐
10 + 10 + 10 + 10 + 10 + 10 + 10 =	☐	10 times 7 is ☐

One way to learn your ×7 table is to add together ×3 and ×4 tables facts.

×3 ×4	Add the answers to build the ×7 table	×3 ×4	Add the answers to build the ×7 table
1 × 3 = 3 1 × 4 = 4	3 + 4 = ☐	6 × 3 = 18 6 × 4 = 24	18 + 24 = ☐
2 × 3 = 6 2 × 4 = 8	6 + 8 = ☐	7 × 3 = 21 7 × 4 = 28	21 + 28 = ☐
3 × 3 = 9 3 × 4 = 12	9 + 12 = ☐	8 × 3 = 24 8 × 4 = 32	24 + 32 = ☐
4 × 3 = 12 4 × 4 = 16	12 + 16 = ☐	9 × 3 = 27 9 × 4 = 36	27 + 36 = ☐
5 × 3 = 15 5 × 4 = 20	15 + 20 = ☐	10 × 3 = 30 10 × 4 = 40	30 + 40 = ☐

You can also build the ×7 table by adding together ×2 and ×5 tables facts.

Multiplying by 7

Write the answers to these multiplications.

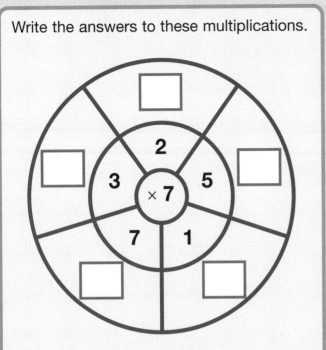

Write the answers to these multiplications.

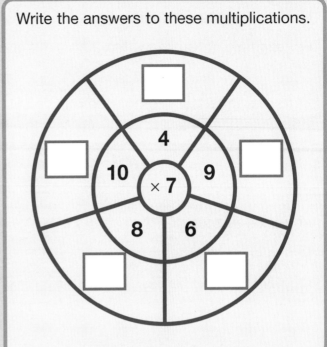

Write the answers to these problems.

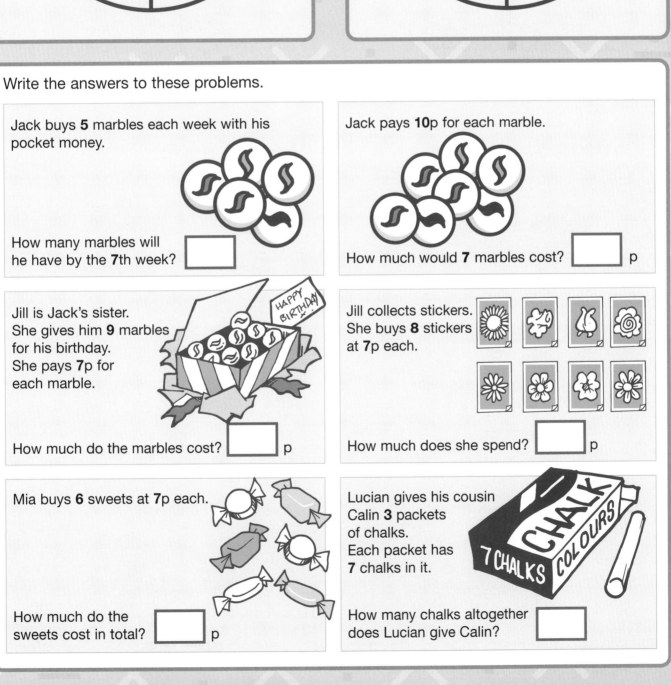

Jack buys **5** marbles each week with his pocket money.

How many marbles will he have by the **7**th week?

Jack pays **10**p for each marble.

How much would **7** marbles cost? ☐ p

Jill is Jack's sister. She gives him **9** marbles for his birthday. She pays **7**p for each marble.

How much do the marbles cost? ☐ p

Jill collects stickers. She buys **8** stickers at **7**p each.

How much does she spend? ☐ p

Mia buys **6** sweets at **7**p each.

How much do the sweets cost in total? ☐ p

Lucian gives his cousin Calin **3** packets of chalks. Each packet has **7** chalks in it.

7 CHALKS   CHALK COLOURS

How many chalks altogether does Lucian give Calin? ☐

Dividing by 7

Use what you know about multiplying by 7 to help you to answer these.

For example, if you know that $2 \times 7 = 14$ you can work out that $14 \div 7 = 2$.

7 flowers shared between 7 vases is ☐ each.

7 divided by 7 is ☐. $7 \div 7 =$ ☐

14 flowers shared between 7 vases is ☐ each.

14 divided by 7 is ☐. $14 \div 7 =$ ☐

21 flowers shared between 7 vases is ☐ each.

21 divided by 7 is ☐. $21 \div 7 =$ ☐

28 flowers shared between 7 vases is ☐ each.

28 divided by 7 is ☐. $28 \div 7 =$ ☐

35 flowers shared between 7 vases is ☐ each.

35 divided by 7 is ☐. $35 \div 7 =$ ☐

42 flowers shared between 7 vases is ☐ each.

42 divided by 7 is ☐. $42 \div 7 =$ ☐

49 flowers shared between 7 vases is ☐ each.

49 divided by 7 is ☐. $49 \div 7 =$ ☐

56 flowers shared between 7 vases is ☐ each.

56 divided by 7 is ☐. $56 \div 7 =$ ☐

63 flowers shared between 7 vases is ☐ each.

63 divided by 7 is ☐. $63 \div 7 =$ ☐

70 flowers shared between 7 vases is ☐ each.

70 divided by 7 is ☐. $70 \div 7 =$ ☐

Multiplying and dividing by 7

Write the answers.

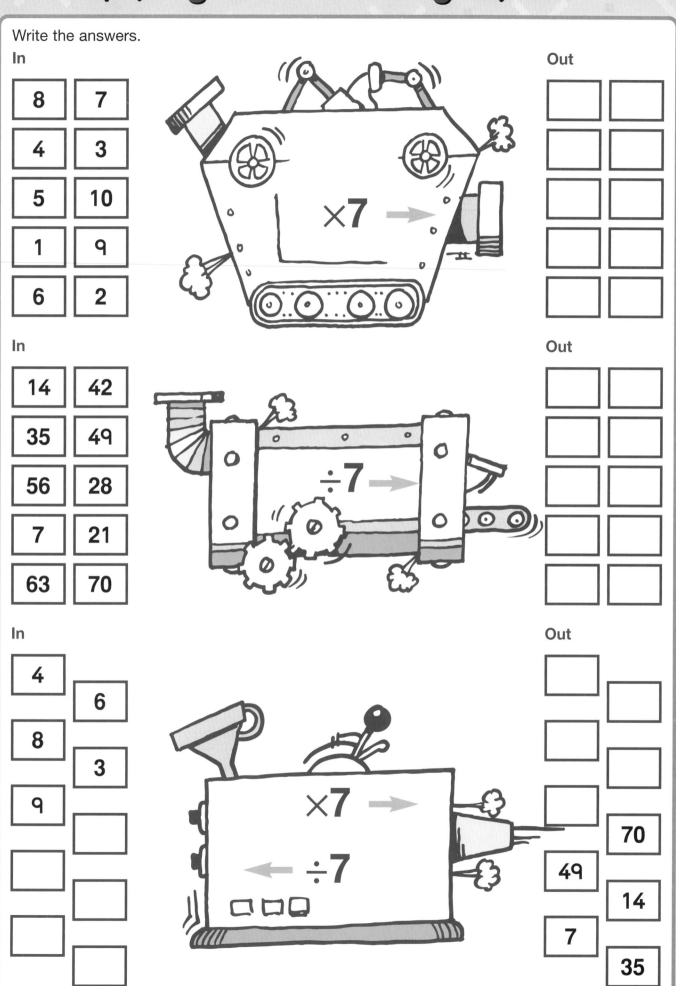

In

8	7
4	3
5	10
1	9
6	2

×7 →

Out

In

14	42
35	49
56	28
7	21
63	70

÷7 →

Out

In

4	
	6
8	
	3
9	

×7 →

← ÷7

Out

	70
	49
	14
	7
	35

Multiplying and dividing by 7

Write the answers to these word problems.

Harry has **35** sweets to share between **7** children.

How many sweets will each child have? ☐

Pranav invites **7** friends to his birthday party. He gives each of his friends **8** sweets to take home.

How many sweets is that in total? ☐

Alana likes to make bracelets. She threads **7** beads onto **6** bracelets.

How many beads does she use in total? ☐

Alice and her mother make some sandwiches for a party. They put out **7** plates of sandwiches. There are **63** sandwiches in total.

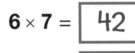

How many sandwiches are there on each plate? ☐

Here is Jon's homework.

Tick the questions that are correct.

Put a cross by the questions that are wrong.

Write in the correct answers.

$6 \times 7 = \boxed{42}$

$8 \times 7 = \boxed{54}$

$5 \times 7 = \boxed{30}$

$49 \div 7 = \boxed{8}$

$28 \div 7 = \boxed{4}$

$63 \div 7 = \boxed{0}$

Schofield & Sims Times Tables Practice Book 2

Multiplying and dividing by 6 and 7

The numbers in the chest are the answers to questions about the ×6 and ×7 tables.

Choose a number and write a number sentence.

Make the number you choose the answer.

Here is an example to help you.

Jane chose 42.

She wrote

$6 \times 7 = \mathbf{42}$

63 54
60   12   56   42
14   49   30
36

 ×  =

 × =

 × =

 × =

 × =

 × 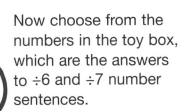 =

 × =

 × =

 × =

 × =

2
7   3
1   8
9

Now choose from the numbers in the toy box, which are the answers to ÷6 and ÷7 number sentences.

John chose 3.

He wrote

$18 \div 6 = \mathbf{3}$

 ÷ 6 =   ÷ 7 =

 ÷ 6 =   ÷ 7 =

 ÷ 6 =   ÷ 7 =

 ÷ 6 =   ÷ 7 =

 ÷ 6 =   ÷ 7 =

 ÷ 6 =   ÷ 7 =

Counting in 8s

Read the numbers.

Write in the missing numbers.

Building the x8 table

Write the answers in the boxes.

$1 + 1 + 1 + 1 + 1 + 1 + 1 + 1 =$ ☐   **1** times **8** is ☐

$2 + 2 + 2 + 2 + 2 + 2 + 2 + 2 =$ ☐   **2** times **8** is ☐

$3 + 3 + 3 + 3 + 3 + 3 + 3 + 3 =$ ☐   **3** times **8** is ☐

$4 + 4 + 4 + 4 + 4 + 4 + 4 + 4 =$ ☐   **4** times **8** is ☐

$5 + 5 + 5 + 5 + 5 + 5 + 5 + 5 =$ ☐   **5** times **8** is ☐

$6 + 6 + 6 + 6 + 6 + 6 + 6 + 6 =$ ☐   **6** times **8** is ☐

$7 + 7 + 7 + 7 + 7 + 7 + 7 + 7 =$ ☐   **7** times **8** is ☐

$8 + 8 + 8 + 8 + 8 + 8 + 8 + 8 =$ ☐   **8** times **8** is ☐

$9 + 9 + 9 + 9 + 9 + 9 + 9 + 9 =$ ☐   **9** times **8** is ☐

$10 + 10 + 10 + 10 + 10 + 10 + 10 + 10 =$ ☐   **10** times **8** is ☐

One way to learn your ×8 table is to double the ×4 table facts.

Complete this table.

×4	Double the answer to build the ×8 table	×4	Double the answer to build the ×8 table
$1 \times 4 = 4$	$2 \times 4 =$ ☐	$6 \times 4 = 24$	$2 \times 24 =$ ☐
$2 \times 4 = 8$	$2 \times 8 =$ ☐	$7 \times 4 = 28$	$2 \times 28 =$ ☐
$3 \times 4 = 12$	$2 \times 12 =$ ☐	$8 \times 4 = 32$	$2 \times 32 =$ ☐
$4 \times 4 = 16$	$2 \times 16 =$ ☐	$9 \times 4 = 36$	$2 \times 36 =$ ☐
$5 \times 4 = 20$	$2 \times 20 =$ ☐	$10 \times 4 = 40$	$2 \times 40 =$ ☐

Multiplying by 8

Join the question to its answer.

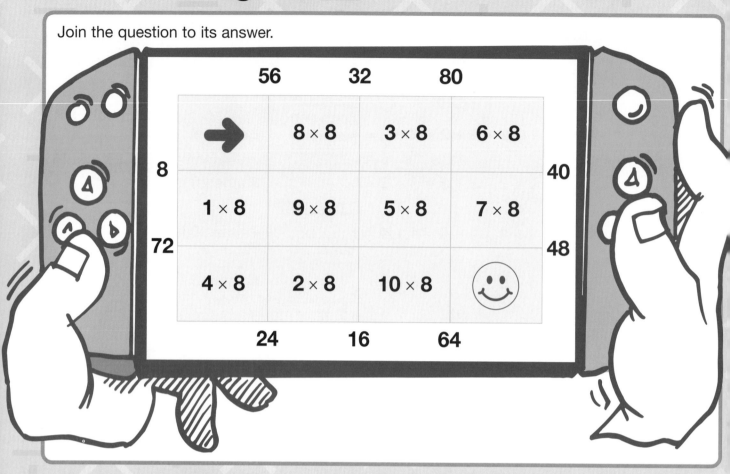

	56	32	80	
8	→	8 × 8	3 × 8	6 × 8	40
72	1 × 8	9 × 8	5 × 8	7 × 8	48
	4 × 8	2 × 8	10 × 8	😊	
	24	16	64	

Write the answers to these word problems.

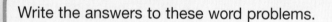

There are **6** tables in the hall.
Each table seats **8** children.

How many children in
total can sit at the tables? ☐

Class 4 is going to the cinema.
Their teacher orders **4** minibuses.
Each minibus will take **8** children.

8 SEATS

If the minibuses are full,
how many children are there? ☐

Dividing by 8

Use what you know about multiplying by 8 to help you to answer these.

For example, if you know that $2 \times 8 = 16$ you can work out that $16 \div 8 = 2$.

8 people shared between 8 cars is ☐ in each.

8 divided by **8** is ☐ .   **8 ÷ 8 =** ☐

16 people shared between 8 cars is ☐ in each.

16 divided by **8** is ☐ .   **16 ÷ 8 =** ☐

24 people shared between 8 cars is ☐ in each.

24 divided by **8** is ☐ .   **24 ÷ 8 =** ☐

32 people shared between 8 cars is ☐ in each.

32 divided by **8** is ☐ .   **32 ÷ 8 =** ☐

40 people shared between 8 cars is ☐ in each.

40 divided by **8** is ☐ .   **40 ÷ 8 =** ☐

48 people shared between 8 cars is ☐ in each.

48 divided by **8** is ☐ .   **48 ÷ 8 =** ☐

56 people shared between 8 cars is ☐ in each.

56 divided by **8** is ☐ .   **56 ÷ 8 =** ☐

64 people shared between 8 cars is ☐ in each.

64 divided by **8** is ☐ .   **64 ÷ 8 =** ☐

72 people shared between 8 cars is ☐ in each.

72 divided by **8** is ☐ .   **72 ÷ 8 =** ☐

80 people shared between 8 cars is ☐ in each.

80 divided by **8** is ☐ .   **80 ÷ 8 =** ☐

Multiplying and dividing by 8

Write the answers.

Now try these.

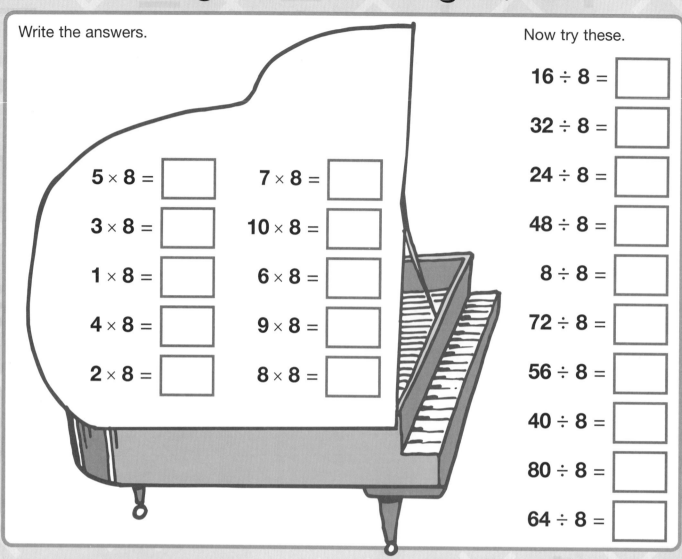

$5 \times 8 =$ ☐ $7 \times 8 =$ ☐

$3 \times 8 =$ ☐ $10 \times 8 =$ ☐

$1 \times 8 =$ ☐ $6 \times 8 =$ ☐

$4 \times 8 =$ ☐ $9 \times 8 =$ ☐

$2 \times 8 =$ ☐ $8 \times 8 =$ ☐

$16 \div 8 =$ ☐

$32 \div 8 =$ ☐

$24 \div 8 =$ ☐

$48 \div 8 =$ ☐

$8 \div 8 =$ ☐

$72 \div 8 =$ ☐

$56 \div 8 =$ ☐

$40 \div 8 =$ ☐

$80 \div 8 =$ ☐

$64 \div 8 =$ ☐

Write the missing numbers.

In

48

72

8

24

64

Out

4

2

10

7

5

Multiplying and dividing by 8

Write the answers to these word problems.

There are **56** children in Year 4.
The children want to go to a concert.
They can travel in minibuses which
hold **8** passengers each.

How many minibuses are needed? ☐

The children go in
groups of **8**.
The concert costs
£**72** for each group.

How much is
that for each
child ?

£ ☐

Each minibus costs £**8**.

How much is
this in total?

£ ☐

The children have ice creams at the concert.
The ice creams cost £**16** for each group.

How much is that for each child? £ ☐

The band performs
3 sets of **8** songs.

How many songs is that altogether? ☐

All the children in one group
buy a souvenir programme.
Each programme costs £**6**.

SOUVENIR
PROGRAMME

How much did the
group spend in total
on programmes?

£ ☐

Multiplying and dividing by 2, 3, 4, 5, 6, 7, 8 and 10

Write the answer in the box.

The answer starts the next question.

Answer these in order.

Start

$56 \div 7 =$

☐ × 3

☐ ÷ 6

☐ × 8

☐ ÷ 4

☐ × 7

☐ × 2

☐ ÷ 5

☐ × 2

☐ × 5

☐ × 5

☐ ÷ 4

☐ ÷ 10

☐ ÷ 5

☐ ÷ 2

☐ × 10

☐ × 10

☐ ÷ 4

☐ ÷ 6

☐ × 8

☐ × 3

☐ ÷ 5

Counting in 9s

Read the numbers. Write in the missing numbers.

0   9   18   ☐   ☐   ☐   54

☐   ☐   ☐   27   36   45   ☐   ☐

0   ☐   18   ☐   36   ☐   54   63   72

18   27   ☐   ☐   ☐   ☐   72   ☐   90

☐   ☐   ☐   27   36   45   ☐   ☐   ☐   ☐   ☐

90   81   72   ☐   ☐   ☐   36   27   18   9   ☐

54   ☐   ☐   ☐   18   ☐

72   ☐   ☐   ☐   36   ☐   18

Start at 0. Count in 9s. Write the numbers in the boxes.

0   ☐   ☐   ☐   ☐   ☐   ☐   ☐   ☐   ☐   90

Look carefully at each of the tens digits. Write what you notice.

☐

Now look carefully at the ones digits. Write what you notice.

☐

Now for each of the counting in 9s numbers add the tens and ones digits together.

Write what you find.

☐

Building the ×9 table

Write the answers. Then check them using these facts about the ×9 table.

- The tens digits go **up** by one as the ones digits go **down** by one.
- When you add the tens and ones digits together they total 9.

$1 + 1 + 1 + 1 + 1 + 1 + 1 + 1 + 1 =$ ☐   1 times **9** is ☐

$2 + 2 + 2 + 2 + 2 + 2 + 2 + 2 + 2 =$ ☐   2 times **9** is ☐

$3 + 3 + 3 + 3 + 3 + 3 + 3 + 3 + 3 =$ ☐   3 times **9** is ☐

$4 + 4 + 4 + 4 + 4 + 4 + 4 + 4 + 4 =$ ☐   4 times **9** is ☐

$5 + 5 + 5 + 5 + 5 + 5 + 5 + 5 + 5 =$ ☐   5 times **9** is ☐

$6 + 6 + 6 + 6 + 6 + 6 + 6 + 6 + 6 =$ ☐   6 times **9** is ☐

$7 + 7 + 7 + 7 + 7 + 7 + 7 + 7 + 7 =$ ☐   7 times **9** is ☐

$8 + 8 + 8 + 8 + 8 + 8 + 8 + 8 + 8 =$ ☐   8 times **9** is ☐

$9 + 9 + 9 + 9 + 9 + 9 + 9 + 9 + 9 =$ ☐   9 times **9** is ☐

$10 + 10 + 10 + 10 + 10 + 10 + 10 + 10 + 10 =$ ☐   10 times **9** is ☐

Another way to learn your ×9 table is to multiply the ×3 table facts by 3.

×**3**	Multiply the answer by 3 to build the ×9 table	×**3**	Multiply the answer by 3 to build the ×9 table
$1 \times 3 = 3$	$3 \times 3 =$ ☐	$6 \times 3 = 18$	$3 \times 18 =$ ☐
$2 \times 3 = 6$	$3 \times 6 =$ ☐	$7 \times 3 = 21$	$3 \times 21 =$ ☐
$3 \times 3 = 9$	$3 \times 9 =$ ☐	$8 \times 3 = 24$	$3 \times 24 =$ ☐
$4 \times 3 = 12$	$3 \times 12 =$ ☐	$9 \times 3 = 27$	$3 \times 27 =$ ☐
$5 \times 3 = 15$	$3 \times 15 =$ ☐	$10 \times 3 = 30$	$3 \times 30 =$ ☐

Multiplying by 9

Write the answers to the number sentences.

6 × 9 = ☐   8 × 9 = ☐

3 × 6 = ☐   1 × 9 = ☐

2 × 9 = ☐   10 × 9 = ☐   4 × 9 = ☐

7 × 9 = ☐   9 × 9 = ☐   5 × 9 = ☐

Write the answers to these word problems.

9 children ride in a minibus.

How many children can ride in **6** minibuses? ☐

There are **9** tables in the hall. **9** children can sit at each table.

How many children in total can sit at the tables? ☐

Halina puts **7** cakes onto a plate. She does this **9** times.

How many cakes are there altogether? ☐

Lukasz brings **8** bags of oranges to school. There are **9** oranges in each bag.

How many children can each have an orange? ☐

Dividing by 9

Use what you know about multiplying by 9 to help you to answer these.

For example, if you know that $2 \times 9 = 18$ you can work out that $18 \div 9 = 2$.

9 people shared between

9 minibuses is [ ] in each.

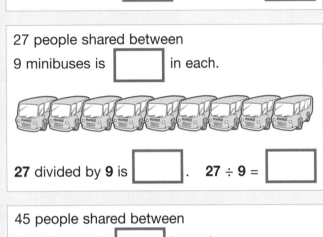

9 divided by **9** is [ ] . **9 ÷ 9 =** [ ]

18 people shared between

9 minibuses is [ ] in each.

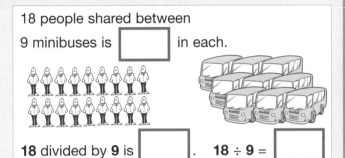

18 divided by **9** is [ ] . **18 ÷ 9 =** [ ]

27 people shared between

9 minibuses is [ ] in each.

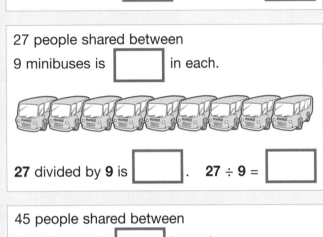

27 divided by **9** is [ ] . **27 ÷ 9 =** [ ]

36 people shared between

9 minibuses is [ ] in each.

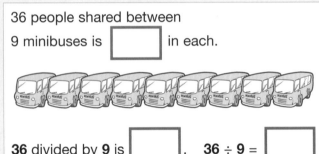

36 divided by **9** is [ ] . **36 ÷ 9 =** [ ]

45 people shared between

9 minibuses is [ ] in each.

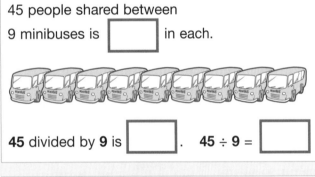

45 divided by **9** is [ ] . **45 ÷ 9 =** [ ]

54 people shared between

9 minibuses is [ ] in each.

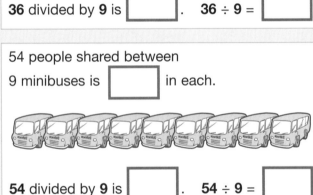

54 divided by **9** is [ ] . **54 ÷ 9 =** [ ]

63 people shared between

9 minibuses is [ ] in each.

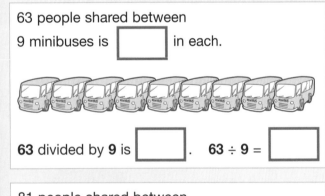

63 divided by **9** is [ ] . **63 ÷ 9 =** [ ]

72 people shared between

9 minibuses is [ ] in each.

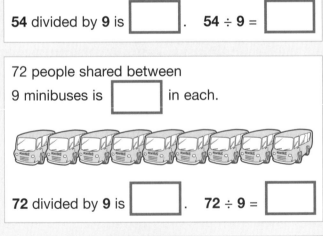

72 divided by **9** is [ ] . **72 ÷ 9 =** [ ]

81 people shared between

9 minibuses is [ ] in each.

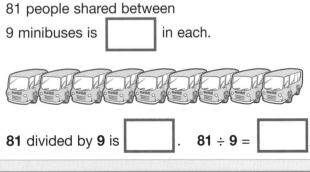

81 divided by **9** is [ ] . **81 ÷ 9 =** [ ]

90 people shared between

9 minibuses is [ ] in each.

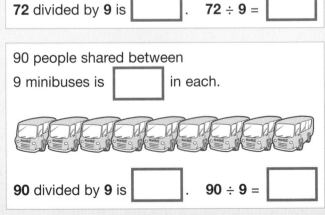

90 divided by **9** is [ ] . **90 ÷ 9 =** [ ]

Multiplying and dividing by 9

Write the answers to these.

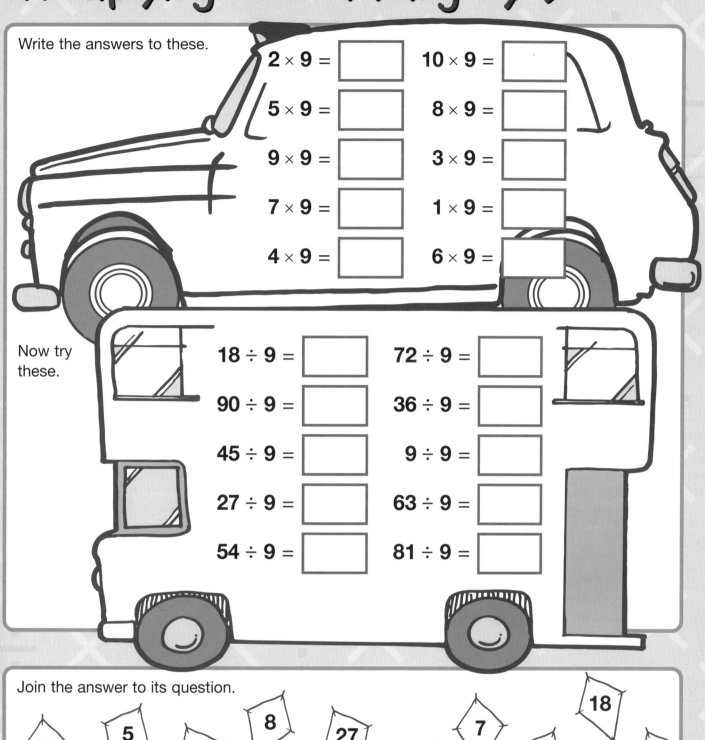

$2 \times 9 =$ ☐ $10 \times 9 =$ ☐

$5 \times 9 =$ ☐ $8 \times 9 =$ ☐

$9 \times 9 =$ ☐ $3 \times 9 =$ ☐

$7 \times 9 =$ ☐ $1 \times 9 =$ ☐

$4 \times 9 =$ ☐ $6 \times 9 =$ ☐

Now try these.

$18 \div 9 =$ ☐ $72 \div 9 =$ ☐

$90 \div 9 =$ ☐ $36 \div 9 =$ ☐

$45 \div 9 =$ ☐ $9 \div 9 =$ ☐

$27 \div 9 =$ ☐ $63 \div 9 =$ ☐

$54 \div 9 =$ ☐ $81 \div 9 =$ ☐

Join the answer to its question.

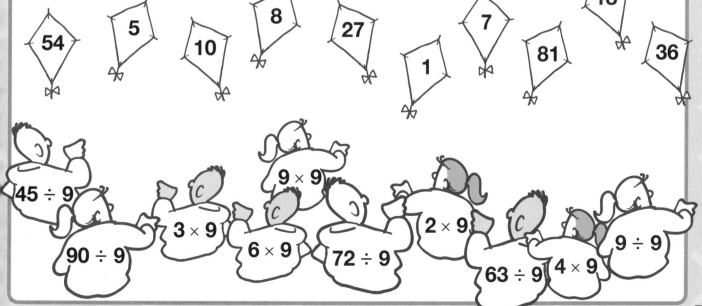

54   5   10   8   27   1   7   81   18   36

$45 \div 9$ 9×9 3×9 6×9 $72 \div 9$ 2×9 $9 \div 9$ $90 \div 9$ $63 \div 9$ 4×9

Multiplying and dividing by 9

Write the answers to these word problems.

Miguel bought a £7 DVD every week for **9** weeks.

How much did this cost him in total? £ ____

Angelita bought **9** CDs at £6 each.

How much did she pay? £ ____

Koji spent all of the money he had saved. He had £**72** in the bank. He bought £**9** DVDs.

How many did he buy? ____

Akiko bought her grandmother **9** boxes of chocolates as presents for family members. The chocolates cost £**9** a box.

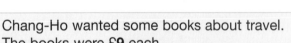

How much did Akiko spend in total? £ ____

Chang-Ho wanted some books about travel. The books were £**9** each.

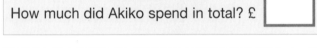

How many books could he buy for £**45**? ____

Sang-Mi has £**36** in her purse. She spends all of it on £**9** books about artists.

How many books can she buy? ____

Problems

Write the answers to these multi-step word problems.

Mark has **6** bags of marbles.
Each bag contains **4** marbles.
He decides to share out the marbles between himself and **7** friends.

How many marbles do they each receive? ☐

Jaycee buys **9** packs of pens.
Each pack contains **4** pens.

If **6** people share out Jaycee's pens, how many will they have each? ☐

Paul has **8** football cards. James has **9** times as many football cards as Paul.

How many more cards has James than Paul? ☐

Lourdes and Antonio each buy some packs of chews.
Lourdes buys **8** packs which each contain **7** chews.
Antonio buys **9** packs which each contain **6** chews.

Who has more chews? ☐

How many more? ☐

Intira has **9** times as many stickers as Orapan.
Sunisa has **7** times as many stickers as Orapan.

If Orapan has **4** stickers how many do Intira and Sunisa have?

Intira ☐   Sunisa ☐

Joshua and Madison share out some small sandwiches with **5** friends.
There are **36** sandwiches on one tray and **20** on the other.

How many sandwiches will each child receive? ☐

What if there were **6** friends and Joshua and Madison.
How many sandwiches would each child receive then? ☐

What I Know

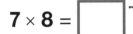

Even adults find some multiplication tables difficult.
Time how long it takes you to answer these questions.

$5 \times 6 =$ ☐ $7 \times 8 =$ ☐ $6 \times 9 =$ ☐

$8 \times 9 =$ ☐ $7 \times 9 =$ ☐ $9 \times 8 =$ ☐

$6 \times 7 =$ ☐ $6 \times 8 =$ ☐ $8 \times 7 =$ ☐

$4 \times 8 =$ ☐ $9 \times 6 =$ ☐ $9 \times 7 =$ ☐

$7 \times 7 =$ ☐ $8 \times 8 =$ ☐ $9 \times 9 =$ ☐

It took me ☐ minutes.

Take the numbers 5, 6 and 30. You know that $5 \times 6 = 30$. So, you can also work out that:

$6 \times 5 = 30$ $30 \div 5 = 6$ $30 \div 6 = 5$

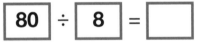

Write the answer to the division sentence. Then write another division
sentence and two multiplication sentences using the same numbers.

$80 \div 8 =$ ☐

☐ $\div$ ☐ $=$ ☐   ☐ $\times$ ☐ $=$ ☐   ☐ $\times$ ☐ $=$ ☐

$63 \div 7 =$ ☐

☐ $\div$ ☐ $=$ ☐   ☐ $\times$ ☐ $=$ ☐   ☐ $\times$ ☐ $=$ ☐

$72 \div 9 =$ ☐

☐ $\div$ ☐ $=$ ☐   ☐ $\times$ ☐ $=$ ☐   ☐ $\times$ ☐ $=$ ☐

$54 \div 6 =$ ☐

☐ $\div$ ☐ $=$ ☐   ☐ $\times$ ☐ $=$ ☐   ☐ $\times$ ☐ $=$ ☐

$56 \div 8 =$ ☐

☐ $\div$ ☐ $=$ ☐   ☐ $\times$ ☐ $=$ ☐   ☐ $\times$ ☐ $=$ ☐